Robert S. Frost & Deborah Baker Monday

Book 1

Mrs. Helen Motter
806 Castle Heights Rd
Bowling Green, KY 42103-8716

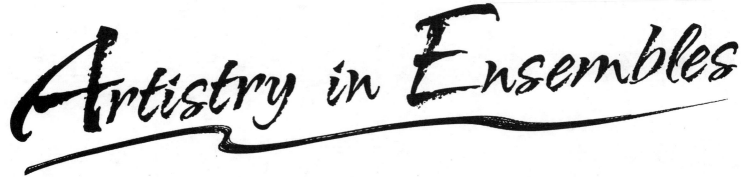

17 Beginning-Level Ensembles
for String Instruments

Contents

D1275192

This book offers two fingering systems. The traditional approach (marked LP for Low Position) is shown on the left page while the Middle Position (marked MP) is featured on the right page. These two systems combine for the 2nd half of the book. On combined pages, LP fingerings appear above the staff and MP fingerings appear below. Roman numerals indicate the strings; I = G string, II = D string, III = A string, IV = E string.

ISBN 0-8497-3425-8

kjos NEIL A. KJOS MUSIC COMPANY • San Diego, California

Hard Rock Highway

Deborah Baker Monday

2nd time - double all quarters (as two 8ths)
3rd time - add rhythm patterns ad lib.

Slower

Hard Rock Highway

Deborah Baker Monday

2nd time - double all quarters (as two 8ths)
3rd time - add rhythm patterns ad lib.

Slower

Vittles Valse

Robert S. Frost

+ Left hand pizzicato. Strum across the strings.

Vittles Valse

Robert S. Frost

+ Left hand pizzicato. Strum across the strings.

Ancient Mother

**Traditional Native American
arr. Deborah Baker Monday**

Ancient Mother

**Traditional Native American
arr. Deborah Baker Monday**

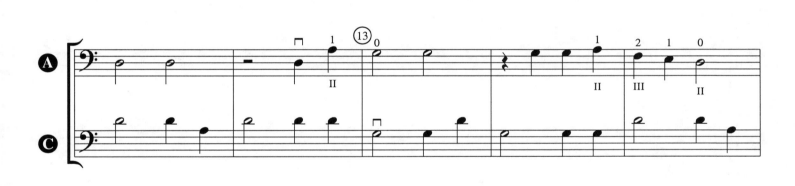

Bolero

Deborah Baker Monday

Bolero

Deborah Baker Monday

Pop, Popcorn! Pop!

Robert S. Frost

Pop, Popcorn! Pop!

Robert S. Frost

Lo Yisa Goy
(A Song of Peace)

Traditional Jewish
arr. Deborah Baker Monday

Lo Yisa Goy
(A Song of Peace)

Traditional Jewish
arr. Deborah Baker Monday

Kutsu ga Naru
(The Sound of Shoes)

Japanese Children's Song
arr. Robert S. Frost

Kutsu ga Naru
(The Sound of Shoes)

Japanese Children's Song
arr. Robert S. Frost

Minuet

Georg Philipp Telemann (1681-1767)
arr. Deborah Baker Monday

Minuet

Georg Philipp Telemann (1681-1767)
arr. Deborah Baker Monday

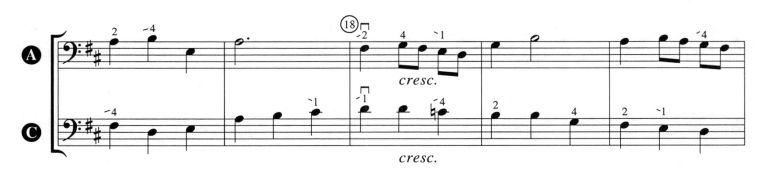

King William's March

Jeremiah Clarke (c. 1674-1707)
arr. Robert S. Frost

King William's March

Jeremiah Clarke (c. 1674-1707)
arr. Robert S. Frost

Ballades of the American West

American Folk Songs
arr. Robert S. Frost

"The Rio Grande"

The Spirit of America
Variations on "Yankee Doodle"

Traditional
arr. Deborah Baker Monday

Chester

William Billings (1746-1800)
arr. Robert S. Frost

Galactic Odyssey

Deborah Baker Monday

* Slide slowly up the string with the 1st finger.

** Play strings behind the bridge.

*** Alternate between the two notes as rapidly as possible.

† Make nontraditional sounds on your instrument. Try tapping the body, sliding the 1st finger up and down the strings, bowing behind the bridge, tremolo, and "snap" pizzicato. Watch the conductor for the cutoff.

Mattachins
(Sword Dance)

Traditional French
arr. Deborah Baker Monday

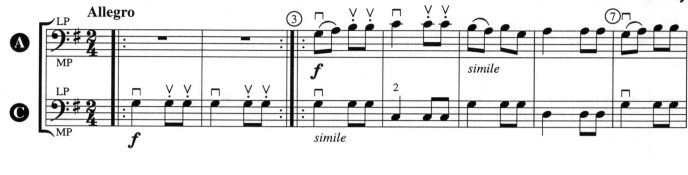

* Lower part is optional.

Engine 91

Robert S. Frost

Festival of Brahms

Johannes Brahms (1833-1897)
arr. Deborah Baker Monday

Shuckin' the Corn

American Folk Song
arr. Robert S. Frost